for Nigel —
— SO years in Whitchurch
from Pea mica mylow

Do Goats go to Heaven?

By Pea Brodhurst

Published by Pea Brodhurst
www.peabrodhurst.co.uk

ISBN 978-0-9926553-0-3

Printed and bound in Great Britain
by NP Design & Print

Acknowledgements

On our behalf Pea would like to extend our thanks to all the following who have certainly given so much of their time and patience in the final polishing of this work. To Robin, Candida, Olivia, Barney, Luca and Sam for accepting the domestic arrangements at the Mill with intermittent displays of patience and thinly veiled tolerance; to our friends within the village, in particular Mark and Jilly, for allowing us grazing, hedge pruning and general foraging on their land. Candida, once again, for her fortitude and competence in the arduous field of design.

Finally Pea and I wish to acknowledge our most heartfelt gratitude to Pea's dear friend Sarah Eason for her help, encouragement, support and ruthless eradication of the semi colon. We stand deeply in her debt for her patience and her time, her skills and her encouragement.

This small book we dedicate to Bettina.

Throughout her darkest days our dear Bettina asked me to read to her, a chapter a day. Her generous enthusiasm and apparent enjoyment gave me so much reassurance. She told me that her great ambition was to live long enough in order to hold a copy of this book in her hand. It gives me such sorrow to tell you that her death came too soon

INTRODUCTION

It has been quite a revelation for me to have discovered that goats are intuitive and highly intelligent creatures, and that their skills in the art of communication appear to know no bounds. It is for this reason that I have chosen to put pen to paper and make an attempt to transcribe the random musings and meditations of my small goat so that I might attempt to throw some light on the general thinking of a goat and give them some sort of a voice.

The choosing of a title for this book has presented me with quite a difficult challenge and so, as many might have been wondering why I have hit upon this one, I shall explain. I was sent, at the age of eleven, to a school which is set on the coldest and windiest hill in the whole of Berkshire, in an appropriately named village called Cold Ash. It was at this school that I discovered the joys of 'writing'. All the subjects that allowed me to paint pictures with pens, brushes and words held me under their spell – each and every other of the subjects allowed me time in which to day dream.

The school was founded in 1907 by a charismatic and most inspirational lady by the name of Olive Willis at Downe in Kent, it opened with only three students and Miss Willis actively encouraged her girls to feel able to set aside self consciousness and develop a sense of free expression. Such an education may well be responsible for the symbiotic respect that I have for goats!

Whilst recently re-reading Miss Willis's recollections of those early days, I noted with a warm flicker of approval, that the most constantly asked question was "Can you tell us please, do you know if goats go to Heaven?"

The season of mellow fruitfullness and a carpet of windfallen apples

How on earth did I happen?

To lose one's mother as a little kid is universally viewed as a tragedy, but in my case her demise opened up the door to a new life of pure indulgence, an abundance of unconditional love and, within reason, all that a small goat could possibly want and expect from such uncertain beginnings.

The facts of my birthright still remain open to speculation. The one thing that we do know is that I was born in the month of August and found myself in a rather bleak and draughty cow stall on a rural and mud-encrusted farm in Berkshire, not a habitat that I would ever choose to return to.

Fairly soon after I had emerged from the warm safety of my mother's womb, I suddenly found myself quite alone. We are told that my mother died and disappeared up to the heavenly pastures. As nothing has been recorded about the identity of my father it is presumed that he must have done a runner pretty swiftly after his amorous encounter with my mother. Left to forage among the chickens, my birth evidently a complete non-event, I found myself to be quite ignored within the day to day life of the busy farmyard.

If the farmer felt any compassion for my plight he masked it well. "If that there kid is gonna avoid the pot we gotta either find some softy to rear 'im or put 'im out there with the 'effers to fend for 'imself" he muttered to his son. This didn't sound promising to me at all, so I made up my mind to keep my head down low and continue to scratch with the chickens in the hopes that I would blend in with the crowd. Certainly, as long as I remained the same sort of size as them, I found that I was able to remain reasonably camouflaged, indeed I soon became wise to the laws of the farmyard.

It was on one warm summer afternoon in mid September that my fortunes took a massive change of direction. A garden fete had been arranged in the village. There were balloons, ice creams, a plethora of frivolous competitions, a tug of war and an unfortunate hog turning slowly on a spit. Instead of racing as intended, all the feisty little terrier dogs were waging battle with a toy rabbit. As an extra treat for the small children the farmer had volunteered to take along a collection of creatures, so I had been boarded onto a farm truck alongside two llamas with nasal problems, a sheep with her two hyper-active lambs and one foul-mouthed goose. We were penned up accordingly and, being still very vulnerable, I was singled out amongst the forty chickens and placed in a compound of straw bales, all on my own, to gaze in horror at a completely new sort of world. It seemed to be a loud and intimidating place to be and, in my panic, I ached for the security of my chicken run.

It was at this point that my world revolved on its axis and landed the right way up! Having heard my pitiful cries, a loud and shadowy figure abandoned her position on the 'knobbly knees' platform and bustled towards me. I soon learned her name, but never really came to understand why she should be called

The proposition of a walk is
not to my liking today

after a very small vegetable. As luck would have it, Pea seemed to tumble headlong for my charms, my quivering little form, my pleading brown eyes and my tangible need for TLC. She scooped me up from my byre and tucked me into her ample bosom as we made our way to negotiate a deal with the farmer. The entire transaction took no longer than four or five minutes, "Take 'im!" he said " 'ees all yours, 'ees no good to me either way!" I think I remember that Pea handed him a bottle of claret in return to ensure that there was no going back on the deal.

In an attempt to provide some sort of thumbnail sketch, I will tell you that this Pea is a woman erring on the wrong side of middle age, a grandmother to a pair of feisty boys and considered by them to display qualities of a capricious nature. Her grown-up children show signs of reacting to her with bouts of intermittent exhaustion and frequent sighs of exasperation. As for me, I *still* find Pea to be without flaw, free of all impediments. She is all, and everything, that a goat could possibly want!

However it became pretty evident on the day of the fete that the threats emanating from Pea's husband were not only falling on very deaf ears but clearly going to be ignored on all fronts. Robin certainly delivered some sort of ultimatum that appeared to hinge on my moving in and his moving out, but I did move in and unsurprisingly he failed to move out. And the outcome is that we all live together in comparative harmony in a distinctive little mill in a distinctive little village in the countryside, although four years later I am still feeling a little mystified as to why he, a grown up man, should be named after a rather small bird.

It soon became a popular topic of conversation in the village. One or two shook their heads in disapproval, others expressed voluble concern as to how, exactly, I might integrate with my new-found family and some even inquired, perhaps a little enviously, whether I had any siblings that might be needing adoption too.

It was Farmer Plank from across the fields who, having had years and years of experience in animal husbandry, bravely stepped forward to voice his doubts on the matter. He happened to meet my Pea as he crossed the path from the pub to his tractor and he spoke out loud and clear. "NOW my darlin', this 'ere goat..... 'ee may be small now, but 'ee be 'livestock', my darlin', LIVESTOCK'! he boomed "Ee'll never gonna settle, you mark my words! I said to your daughter only the other day, I said, 'It's never gonna work!' –" But, I said, you know what? Talking to your Mother... I might as well talk to me own *arse*......!"

Discipline, obedience, good manners are of little significance

Naming me has been a problem for her from the start, and the whole matter has never really been resolved to her satisfaction. I am now approaching my fifth year and still she cogitates on an appropriate name for me and still she finds herself unable to find one. It is almost as if she totally lacks any kind of imagination and, if that is the case, it is all quite sad.

My given name, if I have any sort of bleat in the matter, would have been Peregrine Bartholomew Hedgehog. As things stand at the moment I am referred to as Freddie when things are not going according to plan, and Shreddie if my behaviour is considered to be up to scratch. The name Freddie Belinda Hodgehurst was chosen on the spur of the moment by Pea's friend, that pretty young musician who promised to share responsibility with her and who is now far too taken up with scratching on his instruments in London to follow through on his pledge for my care. From the start this name was much against Pea's better judgement and I think that she just grunted in agreement, distracted by the moment. She and I both privately think that Freddie was both an ostentatious and odious choice on his part and she still feels pretty disappointed with herself that she gave in to him on this life sentence. She agrees that Freddie is both appropriate and quite sweet for little chaps wearing felt school caps, and for pet rabbits too, but not for a goat with attitude. I am really quite contented simply to be referred to as 'the goat'.

Having established all that, I will now begin by apologising for the fact that the first couple of chapters, as a gentle introduction, have been all about me, me, me. In fact, the general gist of the matter is that inevitably this whole small book will be largely all about me, with the occasional reference to others who play 'bit parts' in events relating to my day, but these I will endeavour to keep to a minimum.

I learnt to recognise my name from a very early age and to respond accordingly. That is to say, I may choose to respond, according to my mood of the moment, or I may choose not to respond.

Thus if I suspect that an edible reward is involved, my reaction will be instantaneous and I will be, as they say, 'on the case'. However if my mind is on other things I do reserve the right to bide my time and respond, *or not*, at my own speed. Every so often when I am given an instruction, I will choose to stand completely motionless and unblinking for minutes on end. I rather like to pretend to myself that I am taking part in some sort of tableau, all the while submerged in deep contemplation. When I sense a certain lack of patience brewing up from the opposition, I might decide to whip my head round and give my tail a fierce scratching. This enables me to save face, as they say, and then, very loftily, I might condescend to do as I am asked. It is a recognised characteristic of a goat to allow a period of time in which to cogitate, mull over the alternatives and ponder the possible interpretations before deciding whether or not to carry out an instruction.

My favourite game of hide and seek simply *infuriates* him

My bladder and I share

It is generally understood that goats are unable to be trained but, as a team, we made huge efforts to dispel that myth by embarking on a 'potty training' scheme from day one. Certainly we achieved a result, although it has to be said that my bladder control does tend to be a somewhat 'hit and miss' affair, whilst the showering of pellets is quite a random procedure. My bottom can be compared to a fruit machine with a jackpot result every ten to fifteen minutes, and at times, even every two to three minutes. There appears to be no limit to the quantity of pellets that I can dispense and they just keep on coming. Alternatively, with all the distractions of a journey, I have been known to get to Cornwall and back with only two potty stops and no little incidents whatsoever. The only time we have occasionally become unstuck in this department was entirely one of her own making, a misunderstanding all round. When she and I originally embarked on the 'house training' adventure I was extremely tiny and she made the very silly error of saying "...Now be a good boy!" when she placed me outside the back door and when I obeyed her by trickling a puddle

a lack of predictability

on the gravel, she fed me small treats. Naturally enough every time I heard the 'good boy' words I responded by piddling in frenzied anticipation of a jelly baby, no matter where we were. Hence I 'pee-peed' all over the kitchen floor for having been praised for merely coming downstairs as soon as I was called.

Standing beside the car and hearing the engine running does invariably summon a relatively swift response because it indicates to me that we are about to embark on an excursion. Car journeys give me enormous pleasure and so I always 'pee' very readily before hopping onto the rear ledge of her Smart car. This has become an almost impossibly tight squeeze of late. Judging by the expressions on the faces of those in the other cars on the road it occurs to me that they might have imagined that I have been 'vacuum-packed' into her tiny car. I press my head closely into Pea's neck and, in my ecstasy, I rumble softly from somewhere very deep down in my throat. This rumbling is an expression of pure delight and pure pleasure, somewhat akin to that of a goat-styled purr.

A Kitchen is my idea of Paradise

Casting my thoughts back to those heady days of infancy, I remember well those boisterous after supper romps in the kitchen with her small grandsons, how we used to catapult from sofa to chair, and bounce from table top to sideboard, all in the name of 'winding down' before bedtime. I developed a deep, throaty cackle which incited the children to whoop with delight as we circumnavigated the room at eye level and generally trashed the kitchen, that is until I grew faster than the two boys, when these activities had to be curtailed. Those small boys and I still attempt to knock each others' lights out but this is now considered a strictly outdoor activity and, as often as not, requires a referee. Things have a habit of getting out of hand now that I am both faster and stronger and the contest these days invariably ends in tears. Instead of the traditional ref's whistle, Pea carries a sinister red aerosol which is referred to as 'the dreaded Pet Corrector'. I only need the tin to be waved loosely in my direction to get completely spooked even though I know that it is nothing more than a can of compressed air. The only other time that I am apt to quite forget myself is when she comes to greet me after one of her fairly regular travels 'off campus'. In her absences I know full well that she pines for me just as much as I long for her return. So I always greet her with exhalations of warm breath from my nose for a moment or two until, quite suddenly, I forget my joy at seeing her as the urge to punish and recriminate kicks in fast. So I put myself into reverse, stand tall on my two hind legs and advance sideways to deliver a swift and mighty butt. This done I hope that she can now repent for having abandoned us all and that we can therefore pick up where we left off.

Dogs should have been invented

We unfortunately have two dogs who lay claim to living here in our midst. I would obviously prefer them both to find somewhere else to hang out, or maybe attach themselves to some other faraway pack, but the likelihood of that is, I sense, pretty remote.

I have one recurring fantasy. One dark evening, when they both sneak out to 'do over' a few dustbins, I dream that the lid of one heavy bin comes down on their heads with a mighty crash, and, because they are both chunky sort of creatures, they become intrinsically wedged amongst the rubbish. Along comes the lorry from the council and off they go to some depot of waste disposal four counties away.

In earlier days, I had a mildly appealing idea that I would be able to forge some sort of romantic dalliance with the Spaniel so I made a fairly blatant attempt to woo her with my amorous advances, however I did not waste too much time on this ploy as it became quite clear that she had neither youth nor inclination on her side. I was simply casting my charms to the wind. The Jack Russell terrier, on the other hand, is completely and *utterly* up his own arse so I don't waste any of my emotional energy on him. I have a sneaking suspicion that this alpha male dog could suffer from some sort of inferiority complex caused by his reduced stature, or maybe some inherited

with removable batteries

personality disorder. Whatever his problem, this terrier isn't always terribly nice, and we have resolved to regard each other with mutual disdain.

The dogs don't actually bother me too much. Shared walks are a daily event and I have no problem in recognising that she, Pea, is the undisputed head of the herd, that I come a close second in the hierarchy and that the remainder of the family can continue to jostle for position. Her husband and I will never resolve this dispute about superiority and the problem has become quite an issue. When challenged I invariably come off as the winner as I rise up on my two hind legs, taking a sideways stance and butt him in the shins with all my God-given might. He then emits a deafening volley of abuse and Pea emerges to placate the incandescent old chap by making apologetic scolding noises in my direction. Try as I may to tolerate his displays of irascibility, I find that it is impossible not to react.

My identity is a still an unresolved myth

Although I am often reminded that I want for nothing in my day-to-day regime, I find that she, Pea, does have one nagging preoccupation concerning my wellbeing. It is one of those sort of daily worries that tend to manifest themselves in the early hours of the morning when there appears to be not much else to fret about. It is all to do with the 'herd thing'. It is said that goats, being 'herd animals', thrive only in a community of other goats and should never, ever, be without a goat companion. So every so often she feels beholden to amend my situation by trying to integrate me with other goats, little realising that in my wildest dreams I could imagine nothing worse than sharing my kennel with another goat. It's all to do with her burden of Catholic guilt and, of course, I fully understand that she has only my best interests at heart, but I do find that I absolutely and categorically have nothing in common with other goats.

So, in periodic attempts to assuage her guilt we have to put the whole theory, once again, to the test. We have to set off together, hand in hoof, to various bijoux farm parks and/or village fetes in an exhaustive attempt to get me to grab a handle on some form of goat identity. She has been known to steer my face towards a collection of goats within the confines of a pen so that I can 'eyeball' these creatures, thus giving me some hope of self-recognition. I refuse to fall for this ploy and, instead, head manfully to do some mopping up under the nearest ice cream stall.

An attempt to claim an identity

Just occasionally, we want to wallow in a short spate of heartache and we recall the Pea-inflicted misery of that dark winter of 2010. It was during the middle of a wicked February night that she woke with one of her recurring frets. I was buried in a nest of fresh straw, deep within my kennel and sending a volley of comforting little snores out into the cold night air, blissfully unaware of her sleeplessness. She must have woken up with a mind-set to find something to worry about, *anything* would do, and she would make that her point of focus. In this instance Pea had decided to fret about my welfare. Unable to settle, she got out of her bed and made herself a strong cup of tea. It was at this point that she made the decision. The only fair thing to do, she thought, would be to send me away to live in a compound with other goats at the neighbouring bijou farm park. It would be a more natural environment for me, she told herself, and I would be able to frolic merrily with all those 'ghouls with matted hair and chipped and stained teeth'. By noon the following day all the arrangements had been set in place. She and I set off with my luggage, my comfort blanket and my favourite tin saucepan.

I was allocated a north facing, open-sided stall and expected to share this with three heavily pregnant ewes. With one glance at the sheer malevolence in their eyes I could predict that this scenario was never going to work, not

which fell very wide of the mark

in a month of Sundays. Welcoming they were not. All three regarded me with mutinous glares and cornered me, their heads lowered in undisguised aggression. My life was made a misery as they pushed and shoved, butted, monopolised the food trough and the water buckets, kicked my favourite saucepan from pillar to post and, every so often, conspired to intimidate by chasing me at such a ferocious speed that had us spinning in a whirlpool of fleece and fur.

Our parting on that memorable afternoon was every bit as bad as one could possibly imagine. The incident has certainly left deep and painful scars on both of us. I know for a fact that she always sheds a tear of deep regret when she recalls this parting. As she turned and walked away from me I filled my lungs and let out the longest, loudest and most pitiful of bleats. I never imagined for one moment that she wouldn't weaken to my pleas but she didn't. My cries appeared to have fallen upon her deaf ears and were apparently bouncing off her hardening heart.

So there I was, abandoned and having to fend for myself. It was only at a much later date that she confided in me that she was actually bleating too, deep down inside, even more painfully than I was. She also confessed that she took to diluting her hot cocoa with powerful shots of cooking brandy in an attempt to dull the ache in her heart.

We pined for each other throughout those dark and frosty nights. On alternate days she would come to see me with a bag of my favourite treats. The greedy monsters with whom I shared my stall invariably struggled to get their heads into this said bag by pushing and shoving me out of the way. Then Pea would take me in her arms and we would go for strolls together in the farm park, snuggling in amongst the rabbits, and chatting to the wild boar. However both our hearts were buried deeply within our boots. Those heavily laden stall mates of mine still made no effort to be pleasant or accommodating so I decided to take matters into my own hands by focussing solely on methods of escape. I found that I could jump even the most impressive of barricading, and scale perpendicular fencing with ease. Anything I couldn't climb over I would chew. The nice young men in the green overalls did have to admit, on occasion, that they found my methods really quite impressive for one so small.

However, within the space of ten days I saw to it that this trial period was certainly not going to work, the whole endeavour was nothing short of a disaster and that the time had come to call it a day, admit defeat and go home. There remained nothing for it but to 'pull out ALL the stops' and that is what I did.

It was a Sunday morning, and, hearing her approach (as one does usually *hear* Pea before she comes into view), I let out a volley of complaints. I then became all of a tremble and by the time she put her hand out to me I had become one enormous uncontrollable quiver. I buried my scabby little nose into her leg. Indeed it may have been exactly this small scab, the result of a minor altercation, that compounded the decision. It became evident that an earnest discussion was taking place, Pea was discussing with the farmers the situation and it became apparent in no time at all that I was about to return home! Within minutes, I and my saucepan had been loaded into the car and we were triumphantly bound for the Mill, my cosy kennel and those wretched dogs.

This is called the art of
'one-upmanship'

22

So I am what I am

One thing has been established as a result of this past unhappy experience. That is the fact that, in goat parlance, I am not typical of the species. Yes, I am privileged, and yes, I do have three stomachs which need to be kept filled to the brim with anything and everything that comes within my grasp. Like all other goats, I am remarkably sassy. However, and I thank the ambiguity of my gene pool for this, my eyes are absolutely not goats' eyes. They must have come down the line from some ancestral dalliance with a small horse, because my eyes are dark and shaped like lozenges. This has given rise to much comment and, quite honestly, I am delighted about this because even Pea admits that the normal slitted eye of the regular sort of goat can manifest itself as to be very menacing indeed.

Added to this, my horns have never materialised to anything more than two neat little buds. Soon after my birth the Farmer tied my two tiny bollies into a small knot with an elastic band and as a result they dried up and dropped off. Some peoples' eyes water when they hear this but I miss them not one bit. If anything, such a loss has enabled me to smell, not rank as goats allegedly do, but of sweet new mown hay. This fact delights Pea in a big way, "Go on, *do* smell my goat!" she challenges the disbelievers, "take a good sniff! He smells quite delicious - just like a wicker hot-water bottle!"

A question that crops up with a remarkable frequency, and very often addressed to Pea in a po-faced sort of fashion is "What on *earth* induced you to get a *goat?*" I wonder in my turn why an alternative question isn't directed to me - "How on earth did you find yourself living with an oddball like Pea?". Our domestic arrangements rarely fail to give rise to comment. There are some who appear to find our co-habitation and symbiotic empathy something of a bulky pill to swallow and can barely disguise their surprise. On occasion it seems that our friendship has been met with undisguised disapproval!

However Pea is fearsome in her protective feelings towards me and, on a daily basis, she will defend my corner in the face of caustic comments, wry smiles and raised eyebrows. As we have already stated, neither of us bothers to smile politely any longer at that silly old joke about the perfect recipe for goat curry. Even worse is that old chestnut "Oh look, here comes lunch!" whenever we appear. Pea reacts by manoeuvring her face into the expression of a cold and withering stare, while I simply lift my chin, toss my bat-like ears dismissively from left to right and speed up my trot.

Piddle

Actually, Pea has a most likeable acquaintance who keeps a little goat a bit like me, so now I will describe my meeting with Piddle. This meeting was not an unqualified success, but I think it may have been encouraged to initiate some sort of camaraderie between the pair of us. However, the moment the other goat stepped out of its highly polished car we both realised that this was not going to happen.

Piddle lives with her remarkably flamboyant owner somewhere near Henley, and if any small goat has got its life mapped out and tailor made then this one has. Piddle is reputed not only to live indoors, but with the run of the house, unharnessed freedom in the kitchen and, as if that wasn't indulgent enough, the luxury of having the complete and undivided attention of a 'live-in married couple' to tend to all her needs. The nice young lady takes Piddle for strolls around the garden and the equally nice young man is employed solely to rewire the electrics and make good the damaged 'white goods'. Upon listening in to the conversation, it would appear that this young gentleman is kept pretty busy on a day-to-day basis as the wreckage caused by this goat within the confines of her home apparently knows no bounds. If Piddle can't get out, unescorted, and into some meaty bramble hedge, it is only to be expected that she will sharpen her teeth on the antiques and mince most of the electrical goods.

A meeting was arranged and it was decided that all six of us would assemble for coffee and cake on a Tuesday morning in the car park of the local superstore. So I was vacuum-packed as usual into the small boot of her car and, since it was a warm day, I was allowed the luxury of sticking my head out from the convertible open roof. In Pea's enthusiasm, we probably arrived a bit early and were indulging in a spot of window shopping when eventually a vast and highly polished 4x4 car pulled up beside us. Out stepped this extremely glamorous lady, clad in a fabulous leopardskin trouser suit and followed by her attendants. There appeared to be no apparent sign of the said goat, Piddle. All the greetings took place and I ingratiated myself by permitting fondling, stroking and general admiration without so much as a single head butt. It transpired that Piddle had chosen to remain in her cage in the back of her car, because she didn't 'do' public car parks, and there she remained, her head held aloof and her eyes heavy-lidded in an air of superiority. When she was *eventually* coaxed into climbing out of the car it was with a noticeable lack of grace. I then chose to take my cue from her and we both stood straining on our leads to allow as much distance between us as was comfortably possible, and we avoided all eye contact until eventually the human group decided to give the whole thing up and move into the cafe for their coffee and cake.

According to Pea it was during the conversation over hot coffee that

Piddle's glamorous lady owner enquired whether I too made a habit of swallowing metal staples and devouring the contents of writing desks. The reply was of course "Oh NO! But he so would if he could! But he can't!" Pea exclaimed in abject horror. "And the reason he can't is because I don't allow him to go anywhere near my desk!" The glamorous lady appeared to be quite taken aback and replied in her most exotic Persian accent "But, *my God*, she ... Piddle, she swallow always packets of my metal staples from my staple machine...! *Box after box after box, she take!*" There was a pause, "You know, I already give up the cost of the X-ray machine .....These damned X-ray machines, they cost me a *focking* fortune. You know why? Because how you find a million metal staples in all those stomachs, and in each stomach there is kilo upon kilo of stinking, rotting matter? I tell you, it is a nightmare, a *focking* nightmare!"

If I can see it I will eat it

Here lies an unresolved mystery. As you know, I was not born with simply one stomach like those in the large family to whom I belong. I was endowed with three or four. And whereas I may view this as something of a blessing I am also constantly reminded that, to those around me, this does present something of a blight in the day-to-day scheme of things. When required to keep most of these stomachs topped up on a regular basis I find the process of eating takes up a *huge* amount of my time. It can be likened to the needs of the steam engine which requires constant fuelling if it is to run smoothly. Therefore I consider it my main mission to keep my appetite satisfied. In order to do this I find that I need to consume and digest absolutely everything in my sights, whether it be foliage, bank statements, garments of clothing, or newspapers. I do have a real penchant for plastic bags. This predisposition for reaping anything in my path appears to heighten the stress levels of those around me and, needless to say, can also give rise to throwaway comments such us "Crikey, how that goat has grown!" and " Hell, that sure is one fat goat!" To which Pea will respond crisply "and you too would closely resemble a pouffe on sticks if you ate 24/7". For some reason that is quite inexplicable to me, she is hypersensitive about my size, claiming that I am a pygmy. Whilst others attempt to dispute this theory she resolutely stands her ground on the subject.

Caught in the
act of grazing on
God's lawn

The combined businesses of snacking, foraging and ruminating are, all in all, most time consuming but my main meal of the day is served up at dusk in my customary saucepan. I eat a bowlful of goat meal with a plethora of other tasty and nutritious supplements stirred in. In order to spice things up a bit I have sweetcorn added, lovingly chopped apples and other fruits and sometimes stalks of an indiscriminate variety. Strawberries I like a lot, but if the grandchild gets a hand in the matter he snaffles the red bits and gives me the stalks. Currants, raisins, powdered rose hips, they all go in.

In order to keep the people on their toes I like to busy myself by playing my favourite mealtime game. Usually I will devour the lot in a predictable sort of fashion, but just occasionally I will decide to 'mutiny'. Having clattered my hooves against the glass door to alert her that I am actually *ready* for my supper and now consider things to be running late, she will hastily deliver a lovingly prepared meal in my saucepan, and I will lower my head and glower furiously at the contents. Whether they appeal or not I will fly in the face of my hunger and upturn the whole lot with a loud spillaging sort of sound.

I then feign disgust, scattering the stuff everywhere and, in order to press my point, I 'dribble' the tin saucepan around the cobbled surface of my courtyard. This activity does make a simply horrible, ugly and disturbing racket, but I pride myself in being something of a stickler when I am on a mission to displease.

It is a display of exaggerated disapproval and it does give me a certain sense of power and gratification, but there remains a carpet of wasted food, ready and waiting for Robin to come along at the weekend and take a broom to the yard. The rejected sweepings then get sprinkled into the river for the fish to enjoy and so we start all over again.

As we have already mentioned, the regular comments and so-called jokes that come our way and fall unfailingly flat are those related to curry. Pea has of course, over the years, been offered many and variable recipes for goat curry, but this whole merry quip has become quite threadbare from constant repetition so now both she and I simply yawn and gaze into the middle distance with expressions of undisguised fatigue.

It was on Easter Sunday last year that she took me to chew the cud in the graveyard while she went inside the church to sing songs and chant with the rest of them. The lady Vicar emerged after their party into the golden sunshine and, spotting me working on my third regurgitation of rotting matter, gave a small shriek. She then retreated hastily back inside and started mouthing at the Verger that there happened to be a GOAT outside. There followed a lot of silent mouthing and understated arm gestures, with

31

some frantic head-nodding in Pea's direction. The lady in the long cassock then approached 'you know who' and asked her: "Is that thing yours?" To which she beamed proudly and admitted happily that *it* most certainly was. The Vicar followed it up by asking quite blatantly "How nice, how very nice! And are you fattening him up for the pot?"

It does sometimes occur to me that, fiercely protective as she is, she may well one day quite forget the plot and go on to smack somebody. This could well have fearsome implications so I try to remain optimistic and hope that a woman in her latter years, such as she, will not allow herself to 'overreact' in the face of tactless comments. This could well result in her becoming the shamed faced subject of embarrassing headlines in the local weekly Newspaper that read: "Respectable pensioner accused of committing grievous bodily harm on public footpath following insult to pet goat".

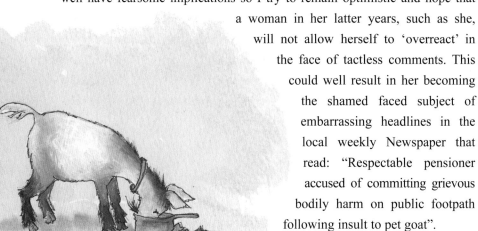

How long does it take to eat a garden shed?

When I declare that I can, and do, eat everything that comes into my path I have to say that, of course, I have preferences within my diet. I am particularly partial to organically grown, sun-dried mangoes, raisins always go down very well, and cashmere jerseys of any colour are quite irresistible. As I have said, the very sight of a plastic bag going spare throws me into an instantaneous 'feeding frenzy'.

Bags invariably cause Pea to spring into immediate action as she once read in a goat self-help manual that a bellyful of semi-digested plastic, however eco-disposable, can result in the speedy death of a goat. With a mouthful of plastic bulging between my jaws, I tear at it loudly to alert her and then make a run for it. As she springs into action I can now guarantee to have her undivided attention. She then runs at me but I can run faster, I have four legs and she only two. Together we sprint, before I dance, spring high into the air and reel off one of my majestic double spins. She soon attempts that well-worn ploy of distraction but that invariably fails in this game so she resorts to 'temptation tactic'. However, as I find that I am now a wiser goat I am also able to win at

Lunch hanging out to dry

34

that game too. I adopt an air of defiance, stand squarely and continue to ruminate on this sodden nugget of plastic, fully aware that I need to keep a good three or four metres between us. My eyes begin to glaze over with the satisfaction of having that ball of warm, wet plastic rolling around in my mouth, so I lose concentration while she suddenly lunges in my direction and rugby tackles me to the ground. There follows an undignified struggle, as a middle-aged grandmother choking on a volley of foul language and interspersed screams of merriment (she still finds my humour irresistibly funny) wrestles shreds of the torn, wet strips from the grip of my clenched jaws.

Although I lay claim to eating anything and everything that will fit into my mouth, I would like to point out that at present I am actually 'working' on the new garden shed. This is huge by any standard so I am viewing it as a long term project. I have already made a fairly impressive inroad into the unsightly construction and the evidence is there to behold: livid scars of untreated wood, bearing testimony to my task, where my front teeth have rasped into both the door and the left hand corner.

I did over the plastic doorknob in the course of an afternoon, but as she did admit that it was a cheap, sub-standard apology for a doorknob on such an expensive erection I was forgiven.

When I moved into this place that I call my patch it was a dappled haven of Mediterranean foliage, a lush, sun-drenched, stone walled courtyard brimming with lusty greenery, an olive tree, a fig, palms of every variety, a couple of garden wall lights to complement the summer evenings and, most costly and mouth-watering snack of all, the electrically powered awning. I had the lot.

Within a matter of days I had reduced this idyllic space to a barren waste of chewed tree stumps and dust. It still remains a bone of contention within the household and causes the family to shake their heads in grave disappointment when they occasionally reminisce as to how wonderful it used to look before I took over.

Anyway *I* very much prefer it this way and I will endeavour to keep it so. To me it has something of the 'minimalist' look, although I did overhear one of them sadly referring to the courtyard recently as nothing more than a 'barren waste land'.

Sleeping is a waste of precious time

Whilst Pea is a committed sleeper, I find that I am a habitual insomniac. Very, very rarely will I tuck my nose into my armpit in order to scoop up forty winks. This is really only after the dawn has broken as I like to 'keep watch' during the hours of darkness. I tend to turn in at dusk and settle myself into my kennel so that I can sit with my nose pointing outwards. I do very much enjoy the company of the moon and I think it must be a mutual thing as I find, quite EXTRAORDINARILY, that my white bits reflect the moonshine in a most striking manner, so much so that I actually glow in the dark. Once upon a time Pea and I went for a long walk all around the fields and woods in the dead of night and absolutely without a torch. Neither of us pitched into a ditch or smacked into a tree because, as she reported with pride upon our arrival home, my glowing presence had lit up our path and acted as a beacon.

There is something that I like very much about the quietness. At times I sit and think but mostly I am aware that I just *sit*. Being a ruminant, I can regurgitate all the previous day's takings and enjoy them over and over again throughout the long night. So, what do I do? I sit and chew, and think, ponder a bit, and chew and chew until the dawn breaks and I am able to start all over again.

I have also often devoted those hours of the long winter evenings to the

Such stillness of the night
allows me the opportunity to mull
over my plans for tomorrow

project of 'ironmongery', namely fathoming the mechanics of door handles and I think that I have at last finally 'cracked it'. What I originally understood to be a masterpiece of engineering devised by man to keep both goats out and the warmth in actually turns out to be nothing more than a sort of 'push and pull' device and one which I find I can now work with ease.

I decided to bide my time so as not to alert any form of suspicion, and then, in the very early hours of a Tuesday morning, I put my plan into action. The whole revelation had come to me during an episode of what they call 'night starvation', when I had a gnawing attack of the munchies and I found myself desperately needing a snack.

So this is how it went. Very cautiously I gripped the said door handle in between my teeth, sucked hard and pulled the thing down until the door clicked open. I then wedged it open with my nose, squeezed through the gap and terribly, terribly carefully I tip-hoofed through their dressing room. I deliberately ignored the wastepaper basket which is usually my first port of call when making a house visit. I proceeded, without making a sound, past their bed (which is on the ground floor between the dressing room and the kitchen). I had anticipated the fact that she might bounce awake if she so much as heard me breathe, so that was a risk that I wasn't even prepared to consider. However I managed to get away with this as they were both clearly quite oblivious to my presence. The rattle of their combined snores was such that, by my reckoning,

39

four small bullocks could have passed them by at eye level and they wouldn't so much as stirred.

Once I had triumphed over that easy hurdle I proceeded to 'work the kitchen'. The room was, as usual, in certain disarray. Although I didn't time myself I imagined that I had a good twenty minutes in which to sort things out. Usually when I made an unannounced house call I gave the game away by setting up a volley of clattering noises which then alerted the family and elicited the cry of alarm in the form of a piercing shriek: "GET THAT GOAT OUT!"

As luck would have it I am fairly familiar with the lay-out of the kitchen so, having established that my time was my own, I started on Pea's latest acquisition, a little dwarf Olive tree in a pot. With a minimum amount of effort I completely cropped the neat ball of foliage and successfully reduced it to a short and naked stump. I then moved on to the basket of farm eggs, not one did I break as I simply rolled them about on the table before moving on to a bowl of damson jam and the bucket of dog biscuits.

The orchestra of rhythmic snoring continued and I must have become complacent, because it was at this point that I made a very poor decision. Having pushed my luck successfully so far, I began to believe that I had become infallible. Upstairs would be my next challenge. Remembering that on the next floor, up above my head, there lay a plethora of delights, a veritable Aladdin's cave, containing mountainous piles of laundry, stacked boxes of Lego and more books to shred than any goat could ever imagine in his wildest dreams.

And this is where I blew my whole plan clean out of the water! I managed to tip-hoof up the wooden stairs with no problem at all, but I had forgotten to take into consideration that it was an exceptionally narrow staircase and that my tummy, by now, had grown to the size of a huge, round and woolly 'pouffe'. As I attempted to traverse the top step I became wedged in a pile of domestic detritus, and, trying to turn around and disentangle myself, I found myself reversing uncontrollably down the very stairs that I had climbed so successfully. I have never managed to master the art of reversing even on horizontal terrain so my rapid descent down the steep wooden stairs in the dead of night

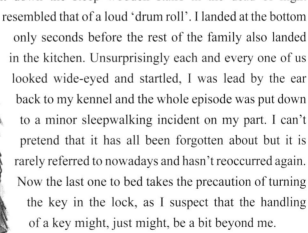

resembled that of a loud 'drum roll'. I landed at the bottom only seconds before the rest of the family also landed in the kitchen. Unsurprisingly each and every one of us looked wide-eyed and startled, I was lead by the ear back to my kennel and the whole episode was put down to a minor sleepwalking incident on my part. I can't pretend that it has all been forgotten about but it is rarely referred to nowadays and hasn't reoccurred again. Now the last one to bed takes the precaution of turning the key in the lock, as I suspect that the handling of a key might, just might, be a bit beyond me.

An unfortunate encounter in a

It was on one bright morning walk that Pea and I happened to chance upon a chap who might well have been my father. We suddenly noticed the backside of something which could well have been mistaken for an old laundry bag, while ferreting deeply inside a hawthorn hedge. It was certainly a very busy sort of backside which, by coincidence, just happened to bear a slight similarity to mine in terms of colour and pattern.

Both she and I stood our ground and eventually a black, grey and white untidy rump reversed clumsily out into the daylight, turned to face us and stared, brazenly, eyeball to eyeball. He clearly did not welcome our intrusion.

"Good Grief!" exclaimed Pea, "Did you *ever* see such a malevolent and wholly unprepossessing creature such as that?

hawthorn hedge

The poor thing really has been 'touched by the ugly stick'".
Unsurprisingly, the mean-looking goat continued to glare
at us with his yellow, slitted eyes, stamping his hoof at the
ground in a most menacing and ill tempered manner. In one
instant I leapt into her outstretched arms, trembling in horror,
and together we made a hasty bolt for the nearest gate.

We were over it without even knocking a bar, but as it
transpired we need not have displayed such blatant cowardice:
the aggressor simply stood his ground, accustomed as he must
have been to commanding hasty retreats merely by casting
one icy mutinous stare. I suspect, however, that the real reason
holding him glued to the spot might have been her reference
to the 'ugly stick' as that remark could be regarded as fairly
offensive even when said in the mildest tone of voice.

44

Seaside holidays, window shopping and social networking

I find that I am a tireless shopper and am always up for any excursion which involves browsing. When I was a much smaller goat Pea used to indulge me by allowing me to accompany her into the shops. However after one particularly frenzied spree in Pangbourne we had to put a stop to that activity and I find that I am now tethered to a lamp post or a bus stop whilst she goes inside and does the business. This makes for an altogether more relaxed outing all round.

Our first port of call on that said morning happened to be the Post Office. All went according to plan until we found ourselves at the till when I became fiercely distracted by the display of shiny and brightly-coloured wrapping paper. The shop, evidently completely lacking in any form of initiative, had mistakenly arranged the tidily balanced display right down at goat level. ...WELL! This, in the eyes of a four-legged novice, was tantamount to 'goat Heaven', a veritable 'pick and mix' store, a temptation to be succumbed to with speed and determination.

I moved in, without a thought for the consequences, filling my mouth in

what little time I had before she brought me down with one of her superb tackles. The display unit came unhitched from its moorings and much havoc ensued but, fortunately for us both, this incident was greeted with a certain amount of hilarity. Clearly the onlookers found this lively pantomime to be quite entertaining, Pea, however, appeared to find the incident less enchanting and had to empty the contents of her purse to pay for all the paper that I had chewed, ripped, shredded or swallowed. Being mildly unimpressed with all this wasted expenditure she remarked that, although she had intended to purchase some wrapping paper anyway, the stuff she'd had to pay for wasn't any use to her at all now that I had reduced it all to pulp.

We then went into the Cobbler and I pee'd to order, as I do, just before entering this tiny space, but once inside the shop I managed to pee again twice in rapid succession. I suspect that my involuntary motions might have been triggered by that heady smell of polished leather, as it is almost unheard of for me to be able to pee-pee three times in one and a half minutes. Both she and I were taken by surprise and she tried to explain this to Mr Briggs as he reached patiently for the large roll of handy kitchen towel, but he looked less than convinced. We kept our visit very brief and moved on to the Bank.

Strangely enough the very same thing happened all over again, but as the counter was too high for them to see what was going on at floor level Pea opted to keep smiling at the nice lady and work the small puddle into the carpet with the heel of her shoe. Then with a slight nod in the direction of the child in the pushchair she gently inferred that there might be a slight problem involving a leaky nappy or some such thing.

"You are like a bloody hot-water bottle with an ill-fitting cap, you are" she hissed at me as we headed for the greengrocer's shop, but I could have told her that this is what goats do and they put it down to excitement.

As I was introduced to car travel at a very early age I find that I am now rather intrepid at it. In fact it actually could be listed as one of my prime pleasures in life. I can truthfully say that 'no distance is too far.' Sadly though the quarantine business prevents me from any form of foreign travel and it isn't just that the 'red tape' complications prove to be too laborious. We have been reliably informed that British goats are simply not welcome on the other side of the Channel. My friend's owner, the glamorous Persian lady, has claimed to have explored absolutely every possible way to get Piddle a flight ticket to her home-land but has drawn a complete blank. It does occur to us that the pair of them might be somewhat blinkered in wanting to take this trip together to a country where goats are prone to ending up in tajins. Fortunately Iran isn't on my wish list of places to go but, there again, Piddle does have foreign connections as we know.

In keeping with tradition we tend to migrate to Rock during the month of July so I am already very familiar with both Port Isaac, Padstow and all those other dear little Cornish hot spots. I have hoofed the miles of that springy turf between Pentire and the Rumps, and can even claim to have broken the British pasty-eating record for small goats at the Atlantic Hotel. On the minus side of seaside holidays though, I have to say that the presence of so much water and soggy sand does somewhat

Listening to the sound of the sea throws my mind into neutral

curtail my enthusiasm. I loathe puddles at the best of times and this one is simply vast. It also makes the sand terribly wet which only contributes even more to the 'misery factor' of beach walking. Having said that, I did take everybody quite by surprise in July by following the family into the sea

on one particularly warm day but the temperature of the water slowed us in our tracks and we found ourselves in that age-old dilemma which is referred to within the family as 'doing a Wilf'.

The sea can appear deceptively appealing and a plan is made to brave the cold water. Everyone strides down the beach in jolly anticipation and all goes well until the cold water reaches the thigh level. This is when the bathers suddenly slow down in their tracks. A decision has to be reached: do they continue to wade in deeper and deeper until they are fully submerged, do they retreat to the comfort of the warm sand, OR do they 'do a Wilf?' If the water level reaches the top of their thighs there will, inevitably, be a very distinctive water mark on the costumes below their waists, a pronounced darkening of the colour which, if they walk back to the shore, may well suggest that they have entered the water for one reason and one reason alone. This is not a good look so the only way to avoid embarrassment is to take a deep breath and DIP. Then nobody is any the wiser!

It was on one of those interminable car journeys back from our holidays that I found myself wanting something to do. We were on our final leg of the motorway, Pea was feeling tired and I was feeling peckish, so whilst poking my nose around in the glove pocket I came across the small change that she hides away for emergency parking situations. I sucked up a pound coin and rattled it around in between my front teeth. She didn't immediately notice so

I swallowed it down and visited the pocket again, and again... and again. After I had swallowed the fourth piece of money she clocked into my folly and from her reaction one would really have thought that I had swallowed the entire set of car keys, fob and all. All hell broke loose, and it's a pretty confined space in that Smart car in which to indulge in such wild arm-flailing, exaggerated gestures, yelling and general lashings out. She called me all sorts of names, but by the time she managed to spot a small lay-by in which to pull over and calm down I had managed to knock back the equivalent of almost ten pounds.

Back home I was promptly marched into the vet's surgery, where Pea demanded that I have an enema. "I want my money back" she said selfishly, going into all sorts of details regarding the big, eye-watering question of my eventually 'passing' these indigestible pieces of metal. His reluctance on the matter was, we agreed, surprising. An enema is, by all accounts, a relatively simple procedure but the vet explained to Pea that all her money would be stored quite safely in a pocket of one of my multiple tummies until such time as I 'move on to the Heavenly pastures'. My digestive system is reportedly not unlike that of the dust bag of a vacuum cleaner, being designed by God to hold on to stubbornly impassable objects in a specially made little pouch for reasons that he preferred not to go into.

Visits to the Vet's Surgery

My visits to the vet's surgery guarantee us all an action-packed morning and provide me with a platform on which to display an example of smug behaviour. My entrance through the front door always ends with a satisfactory result, as when I trot imperiously into the waiting room ALL the other patients, boxed or not, hurl themselves into excessive exhibitions of frenzied bad behaviour. They have a head start as clearly their nerves are already in jangling mode, so I trot in passively and obey Pea's command to sit quietly under the chair and wait my turn in the confined space of the waiting room. With this, they all proceed to 'kick off'! A veritable cacophony of barking, growling, meowing and snapping at the hands that feed them erupts as all hell breaks loose. The veterinary man in the white overall opens his surgery door a crack and remarks "AH, I had a suspicion that *you* might have arrived!" By this time all the owners are apologising profusely to each other for the behaviour of the creature that is on the end of its lead or in its box. Various plastic chairs have been upturned in the frenzy, many of which are caught up in a network of tangled dog leads and dragged noisily around the waiting room. Surveying the pandemonium I remain beside the sole upright chair chewing passively on a mouthful of hedge that I had harvested on my way up the hill.

These wallys appear to
have sidelined the joys of
a visit to the vet

If a goat could blush

The landlord of the pub recently suffered a major 'sense of humour failure' and has now declared his hostelry to be a 'goat-free zone'. I consider this to be a pity for goats because this drinking establishment may now be considered to have become elitist and in today's age of political correctness this doesn't really sit well with me. Dogs, *all* dogs, however bourgeois, always appear to receive a sickeningly warm welcome in that place. All sorts of unruly and unattractive canine behaviour appears to be perfectly acceptable and this doesn't sit well with me *either!* This pub is a place that the family like to frequent on a summer's evening, so either I get left at home, or I am tethered to the telegraph pole outside. I receive an enormous amount of attention and admiration from the other customers there so it's not all bad. To a small degree I might be forced to admit there was an occasion when the landlord could have argued a case to bar me from his pub and I would have confessed and held up my hoof, but it was a 'one off' and, at the time of the incident, nobody had yet bothered to point out to me the general code of behaviour accorded to such a place. The whole episode can be blamed, yet again, upon temptation and it involved a packet of salt and vinegar crisps. I fully accept that I did act on impulse. I became hideously distracted by the heavenly whiff of this packet which some joker had opened and left on top of the bar. The whole tantalizing smell caused me to quite forget myself as self-control flew out of the window and, with one mighty spring, I landed astride the bar, coming to rest amongst a nest of half-empty glasses. A veritable tsunami of beer then caused me to perform a mighty skid and I managed to clear the contents from the length of the bar to the sounds of splintering glass. Suddenly the crowd fell silent, there was a heavy pause of horror and all eyes turned to view the reaction of the landlord. It was a reaction that was worth waiting for, but Pea and I were long gone - we legged it at speed.

Wellies all look the same to me

I have come to discover that the human race, as a whole, is a remarkably cheerful breed. Cars, vans and tractors pass us frequently and all the people within appear to grin from ear to ear, shoppers in the market place chuckle happily and hikers and walkers invariably stop to pass the time of day. "Oh dear God!" groaned Pea's daughter, "How LONG does it take to buy two melons and a French stick?" as we commented on the persistence of the rainfall with every shopper in the Corn market.

On the other hand I cannot claim in all honesty that our occasional encounters with Royalty have been entirely successful. We tend not to dwell on such events as they sometimes seem to reflect on me in a somewhat unfavourable light.

Whilst out on a crisp afternoon walk with Pea and the tiresome dogs, we happened to notice that we were on a collision path with a young couple and their pack, but what she didn't do was warn me, sotto voce, of this little party's notoriety. I feel that she could have whispered something about minding my manners or 'remembering just who you are for five minutes' but no such advice was offered so we met this group of walkers head on. Whilst they greeted each other and commented, yet again, on the persistence of the rainfall I naturally opted to take it out on their fluffy black dog which had circled me in an attempt to sniff my bottom in an invasive sort of way. I don't terribly take to black creatures as it happens, not on grounds of 'colour' but simply because they seem to have no definable features of identification. I find the mass of one colour confusing and cannot tell easily which end is which. As I felt distinctly disinclined to allow this undersized creature anywhere near my tail end, I rose high onto my hind legs and together we entered into a dance of ever-decreasing circles. I promptly received a swift swot on the nose, with everyone smiling politely as the party disbanded, each to their own direction. As soon as we were out of earshot Pea gave me both barrels! She unleashed a volley of retribution and reminded me, as is her wont, that such shabby behaviour is unacceptable on all levels.

To me ALL black dogs look EXACTLY the same, so how was I to know that this particular one was branded with a Royal crest, the future mother of the next generation of spaniels who would live in a castle? Was I really to be so streetwise and well-versed in the world of country ramblers to be able to differentiate those two from the rest of the hikers that walk about our countryside. The fact that he happened to be a Prince and she a future Queen was of absolutely no consequence to me at the time. I shall, in future, sidestep *all* black dogs on the grounds that one never knows what hazards lay ahead.

The remainder of the afternoon's walk was continued in an icy silence, and she now holds me wholly responsible for the fact that we were not invited to a particular wedding ceremony at Westminster Abbey.

The whole Royal Wedding event caused major disruption down here within the muddy wastes of Berkshire. From the moment it was announced to the world that Prince William intended to make the pretty Catherine his bride all hell broke loose. The roads, the kerbs, the pubs, and the footpaths became gridlocked with sightseers and paparazzi all wanting a picture or a tiny tit bit of gossip, while nobody in the village was prepared to give much, if anything, away. I, on the other hand, found myself not averse to the occasional photo opportunity, appearing here and there on the pages of various tacky tabloids with my most memorable publicity a less than complimentary write-up on the fourth page of the Times.

The villagers had become reluctant to get embroiled in interviews with the press and as a result the reporters had found it hard to cobble together any form of copy. However, it was on a late November afternoon that there came a discreet knock on our front door, announcing the arrival of a reporter from a more upmarket newspaper.

Pea picked her way carefully through to the door, to find herself face to chest with what appeared to be a headless man. He was so very tall that his chin might well have been resting on top of the porch. He appeared to be in a state of some agitation and was full of apologies, explaining that he had spent five fruitless hours in the village pub working his way slowly through a baguette with nobody to talk to. I could hear Pea taking it upon herself to offer him a cup of tea in sympathy with his sorry situation. "Well, regrettably the only member of this household who has had any form of 'royal' encounter will be quite unable to be of any help," she offered. There was a brief pause and Mr. Malvern's face lit up like a Christmas tree. "Ah, so there IS somebody...!

BRING HIM ON!" He beamed in anticipation. "Maybe I might be able to winkle even a 'one liner' on the couple, do you think?"

She tried to explain to him in an attempt to deflate his excitement that she was doubtful that he would get much of any significance out of him. "They really only ever cross paths on walks, and when they do meet he is not always exactly reliable in his attitude and behaviour towards the betrothed couple" she continued. Knowing full well that nothing good could come out of this encounter, she came out to my kennel and asked if I might be prepared to talk to the Press. I mulled over the proposition for a while and duly followed her into the kitchen.

Pea gently explained to Mr. Malvern that an 'encounter with a goat' whilst out on a walk wasn't probably high on the wish list of the royal pair. The last one having warranted a swift smack on the nose as I rose onto my two hind legs and danced menacingly sideways towards the Prince in a display of intimidation and superiority. It may well not have been an altogether pleasing encounter with His Royal Highness and Catherine but neither Pea nor I thought that I really deserved the headline in the Times the following morning "Republican goat intimidates Prince William and Miss Middleton with bullying tactics."

It is said that goats are like Marmite

I have heard it said that people's attitudes to goats can be compared to their opinions on the taste of Marmite. This could be seen as something of an unflattering observation but now that it has been gently explained to me I think that I have begun to understand. Apparently humans view Marmite as something that one either loves with a passion or finds quite repellent. I am now relatively OK with this somewhat derogating comparison because I happen to remain secure in the knowledge that I am an immensely valued member of the herd. Judging by the reaction that I draw from the general public when I am out and about, I am left in no doubt that a few people appear to view me as something of a curiosity, this reaction seems to me to be quite curious in itself. I almost always see huge smiley faces sporting rows of teeth in cars as they pass, on the street and in the fields whilst we are out on our walks. Lots of these people point their tiny telephones at me in an attempt to capture my good looks, but I have now learnt to 'eyeball' the lens and the moment I hear the soft click I SWING my head over my left shoulder in the opposite direction. This then prompts my crooning audience to make a second attempt, and then a third and a fourth, by which time I have a tight hoof on the whole scenario and am firmly in command.

A greeting that I hear regularly from small children is delivered in a whining sort of bleat and sounds like "Oh Mummy..! That is so SO sweet, Mummy, Mummy..... Why can't we have one of those?"

Invariably the Mother replies "....We'll talk about that later darling, let's ask Daddy when he gets home," and I say, sotto voce, to myself "yeah, right on....! 'Cos you wouldn't BELIEVE HOW MUCH TIME, ATTENTION AND FOOD I DEMAND! I can, and will if I were to be given the opportunity, munch my way through three gardens a day, chew my way out of every compound to seek for your school uniform, pens, biros and even your pencil boxes too".

I can hold this stance until the clicking noises stop

As things have worked out this end, it has to be said that goats do make happy little pets, BUT, being both strong willed and knowing creatures, we do demand a considerable amount of care and attention on a daily basis. Fresh drinking water is essential as, however thirsty, we will always turn up our noses at a dirty water bowl! Even one dead fly floating on its back on the surface will cause us to recoil in disgust. Clean straw, a perpetual supply of green grass, foliage and lots of conversational interaction with the family are all vital to our happiness.

The other impressive factor that has to be recognised is that we are endowed with a mind-blowing capacity for investigating and devising methods of breaking free. In a goat's world no challenge is too great when it comes to the art of escapology. If the grass appears to be that bit greener on the other side

of the fence then that is where we little goats will find ourselves, our ingenuity knows no bounds.

When it comes to manipulation I can resolutely wreck even the most finely-honed plans by simply refusing to comply. If and when I choose to dig in my hooves and stand my ground, I can remain resolutely rooted to the spot whilst I cogitate upon the matter. Persuasion, negotiation, displays of irritation and edible bribes are as ineffective as blowing bubbles into the wind, and invariably I will only admit defeat as the result of an out-and-out 'stand-off'.

There is no such thing as a pattern of standard behaviour in a goat's vocabulary; everything depends, quite simply, on the mood of the moment. Predictability is not a word that I even recognise. I pride myself, however, on running an exceptionally wide spectrum when it comes to my intention as to what to do next. I will confess to being mild and malleable when I am with Pea for reasons that I put down entirely to instinct. Firstly, she tends to my every whim so it is in my best interest to keep her on side. Secondly, for all her years, she is a pretty demanding cookie, so when the going gets really tough she still attempts to punish me by clamping my head between her thighs and lifting my back legs up to her chin. We remain in this rather humiliating stance until I have no option but to agree that, maybe, I had got things wrong and that, maybe, I could do better next time.

I can't imagine that this undignified form of retribution will continue for much longer as she already claims to be suffering from age-induced muscle degeneration while I, still in the prime of life, go from strength to strength. It can only be a matter of time before she gives up and resorts to her last reserve which is a tirade of strong language and hollow threats.

Goats are canny little creatures, resilient and intuitive. Within that hard little skull there lies a sharp and wily brain, and an attitude of 'knowing equality'. Ever since Pea and I embarked on our shared lives together she has been on a mission to defend our reputation. Goats have been misunderstood and much maligned ever since they were invented. By and large goats have been given a fairly bad press by the Bible and sacrificed at every opportunity. They were hurled off high towers by the Spaniards who must have misguidedly believed that goats had an ability to participate in some sort of wingless flight. It is said that the tummies of goats make formidable 'water carriers' and, worst of all, the very same tummies have actually been used in the bagpipe making industry.

The gift of a goat from above.

Before I was even conceived, during those dark days of 2007, Pea and the family had been having a pretty ragged sort of time and had been confronted by a roll of sad and difficult events. Parts of the house had been flooded in a particularly heavy deluge of rain and Pea had lost every single page of her portfolio, the only evidence of a thirty-year career in painting. She had subsequently been laid horizontally for seven months with a unidentifiable toxic disorder. If that wasn't enough, her dear and much loved mother took the family completely by surprise by dying suddenly in the middle of the night.

So many sad events were, at the best of times, quite hard to process but the month had been January and the short dark days made recovery a slow and arduous process. It was early one morning that Pea felt inside a gnawing anxiety: a feeling of her mother's disquiet and unexplainable nearness, an anxiety that there was still something unresolved hanging in the air. In the light of this underlying concern, she decided to seek the help of a Medium, frowned upon, she knew full well, by the Christian Church. Managing to convince herself that in the circumstances and just this once, she might risk breaking the rules, Pea somewhat tentatively, dialled the number of a reliable Medium who she knew to be a strong Christian believer. Apologetically he explained that he really wasn't free to see her for at least three months as he was much in demand

and his diary was full. He did however indicate that he might be able to help her at an earlier time if she would consider agreeing to a telephone consultation. She expressed a certain amount of doubt that this idea could possibly work, but thought, in the circumstances, that she was quite happy to give it a go. "I can't guarantee success but it *can* work, and occasionally it does... would you be prepared to let me try and see if I can help you in this way? "

Pea hesitantly agreed. "But before you hang up I will simply ask you to give me your Christian name. I don't want to know any more than that, I actively don't want to know where you live and I certainly have no need to be told what is troubling you. Simply give me your first name so that I can put it, along with a time and date, in my calendar".

A month later Pea called this man at the appointed time. They chatted for a short while before he asked her if she would mind him beginning with a prayer. Almost immediately the man said quite distinctly "I am seeing a wicker basket, a sort of hamper – I can't quite make this out but, very definitely, it is here in front of me!"

He continued on other things, all of which were strangely correct, and then returned to the wicker basket. "The basket is still here beside me, it is really rather beautiful and it is lined with white muslin. It is filled with love but, whilst I cannot understand the significance of it, I wonder if its presence means anything to you? Could it be the birth of a baby I wonder?" he inquired. Pea held her breath and, after what seemed an interminable pause, she whispered, in disbelief, "No – I buried my mother in a hand-woven wicker basket, and it was lined in soft white muslin".

He appeared to be a good man and a man with a great faith in God and eternity. Their conversation was intense, positive and remarkably reassuring to her in this dark time.

Towards the end this man reassured her and he said "I will tell you something. You are undeniably suffering over the loss of your mother and you are also, at the moment, very sick and very weak. However it is imperative that you believe me when I tell you that you have a very considerable army of support from within the Spirit World". He paused for a moment, continuing "You have so many loved ones who are carrying you at this time, they are holding you and caring for you. These days will pass and, in the course of time, you will receive two legacies that will be of great significance to you, in fact I will tell you that when you receive them you will accept them both as endorsements of your faith".

The man continued "I will tell you that there are two gifts coming to you, both are legacies sent to you by the Spirits that are from the other side. I must stress that they are not, either of them, of any monetary value. One of them will come as a surprise from another part of the world and you will receive it in three days time......" Pea intercepted in amazement "....But it has already come"!" she told him "it arrived three days ago!" This gift came to her in the form of a package from her cousin in Vancouver. Gill had telephoned a month earlier to remind her of a triptych that had hung beside their grandmother's bed during her lifetime. After her death it had found its way to Canada where it had been hanging in Gill's house for the past twelve years. Maybe she said that she had felt uncomfortable about owning it and had been feeling an urgent need to send the triptych on to Pea, explaining "you and Grannie were always so very close and I feel that she is asking me to hand it on to you. I want you to have it and I think that you should hang it near to your bed". This seemed to Pea quite remarkable and a most precious gift.

The man then continued, but with a discernible note of laughter in his voice, "And the second gift will not be arriving until a much later date. I can't put a time scale on it but certainly it should be with you before the end of the year." He then laughed out loud. "I simply cannot explain any more than this, as it is so very unexpected and, I have to confess, a rather original gift, but when it does arrive you will recognise it as something of great significance!"

This is where I come in! Pea had been the first to admit that she never, ever, put the gift of a goat on her 'wish list'. It had never been her intention to own a goat. In truth the very thought had never so much as occurred to her!

It was only on that warm September afternoon, at the Dingley village fete, that such a decision had been made and, without so much as a moment of indecision, she and I had found our lives so intrinsically entwined!

Weeks went by, as did months, and so the seasons changed. Only then did it all begin to come clear as Pea was visiting her very old uncle. Martin, a retired GP, had lived his life in a remote little hamlet in the wilds of Derbyshire and so their meetings were few and far between. After a long and happy lunch he said to her "Now darling, it is time for me to take a nap, as is my wont, and I will leave you to sift through the family photograph albums, as you have asked." So she curled up beside the fire and proceeded to dip into the dog-eared books. On the second or third page of faded, yellowing pictures she came across a collection showing her mother, her siblings and the family pets in the gardens at Harrow-on-the-Hill. There was Rufus, the legendary Irish Wolfhound, and Jack O'Lantern, the miniature pony who died on the frozen lake, and in every photograph there were two small pygmy goats, each one wearing a smart leather collar and standing proudly in their midst.

When the old man awoke, Pea asked him excitedly, "Uncle Martin, dear Uncle Martin! Tell me something..... Think hard! Can you remember, all those

71

years ago when you were children, back at the Park....? Can you recall ever having little goats as pets?" Uncle Martin thought hard and, scratching his head, he slowly recalled. "Ah, yes! Of course, I do remember! I remember very clearly that my mother, your grandmother, did have a passion for little goats. She always kept a couple of that small pygmy kind. Oh, she was terribly in love with her goats!" His face broke out into a huge grin of happy reminiscence and he threw back his head and laughed. "She kept them at the bottom of the garden and they lived with us as part of the family, as did the dogs and the pony. I think we even took them all away with us on our holidays to Cornwall long before the war!"

So here we have the conclusion of the legacy predicted by that medium a year or so earlier. Pea and her grandmother, until the time of her death, had shared an exceptionally close and loving friendship. Together they discussed not only the meaning of life and the possibility of a life after death, but the presence of Angels, Spiritualism and the existence of God Himself. Both as a child and a teenager she had always said to her grandmother "Grannie, IF you die before me and IF there is a life after our deaths, and IF you do find out what does go on up there, will you send me a sign, a message or at least something to reassure me that even though I can't see you I know that you are with me?" Her grandmother smiled, "Darling! If there is, and if I do, and IF I can, I will... I promise!"

Many years went by during which Pea had her good times, her bad times and even some very difficult times. As she emerged from the bleakest time of them all it seemed to her that, at last, her grandmother had fulfilled that promise made so many years ago. She sent to Pea that legacy in the form of a small goat! A sign, maybe, that could well endorse her chosen belief that perhaps the spirits in Heaven really do watch over us, that still they retain a sense of fun and that there is confirmation for those who believe in a life of Eternity.

After all, what legacy could possibly be more reassuring than a small goat with lozenge-shaped eyes sent from Heaven?

Am I really a gift from the other side of time?

Maybe our circumstances could be considered, by some, to err on the side of the unconventional, mistaken, indulgent, even eccentric. The older I get, the more firmly I believe, and the fiercer I become in my defence of the argument that animals do have souls, that animals have both opinions and feelings, that animals have the ability to feel both sadness and delight. There is so much that has yet to be explained, and how exciting it will be when this big mystery becomes clear to us, not in this world, but in the next. Perhaps a big surprise awaits us all and our beliefs may become apparent!